THIS WHERE'S WALLY? BOOK BELONGS TO:

_____

_____

HEY, WALLY FANS! FIVE INTREPID TRAVELLERS ARE LOST IN EVERY SCENE! CAN YOU FIND THEM?

ODLAW   WIZARD WHITEBEARD   WENDA   WOOF   WALLY

AND IN EVERY SCENE, THE TRAVELLERS HAVE EACH LOST SOMETHING PRECIOUS! CAN YOU FIND THEM TOO?

WALLY'S KEY   WOOF'S BONE   WENDA'S CAMERA

WIZARD WHITEBEARD'S SCROLL   ODLAW'S BINOCULARS

For my parents

First published 1988 by Walker Books Ltd
87 Vauxhall Walk, London SE11 5HJ

This edition published 2015

2 4 6 8 10 9 7 5 3

© 1987 – 2015 Martin Handford

The right of Martin Handford to be identified as author/illustrator
of this work has been asserted by him in accordance with the
Copyright, Designs and Patents Act 1988.

This book has been typeset in Wallyfont and Optima.

Printed in China

British Library Cataloguing in Publication Data:
a catalogue record for this book
is available from the British Library.

ISBN 978-1-4063-6118-6

www.walker.co.uk

WHERE'S WALLY NOW?

MARTIN HANDFORD

WALKER BOOKS
AND SUBSIDIARIES
LONDON • BOSTON • SYDNEY • AUCKLAND

HI THERE, BOOK WORMS!

SOME BITS OF HISTORY ARE AMAZING! I SIT HERE READING ALL THESE BOOKS ABOUT THE WORLD LONG AGO, AND IT'S LIKE RIDING A TIME MACHINE. WHY NOT TRY IT FOR YOURSELVES? JUST SEARCH EACH PICTURE AND FIND ME, WOOF (REMEMBER, ALL YOU CAN SEE IS HIS TAIL), WENDA, WIZARD WHITEBEARD AND ODLAW. THEN LOOK FOR MY KEY, WOOF'S BONE (IN THIS SCENE IT'S THE BONE THAT'S NEAREST TO HIS TAIL), WENDA'S CAMERA, WIZARD WHITEBEARD'S SCROLL AND ODLAW'S BINOCULARS.

THERE ARE ALSO 25 WALLY-WATCHERS, EACH OF WHOM APPEARS ONLY ONCE SOMEWHERE ON MY TRAVELS. AND ONE MORE THING! CAN YOU FIND ANOTHER CHARACTER, NOT SHOWN BELOW, WHO APPEARS ONCE IN EVERY PICTURE?

Wally

2,000 YEARS AGO

FVN AND GAMES IN ANCIENT ROME

THE ROMANS SPENT MOST OF THEIR TIME FIGHTING, CONQVERING, LEARNING LATIN AND MAKING ROADS. WHEN THEY TOOK THEIR HOLIDAYS, THEY ALWAYS HAD GAMES AT THE COLISEVM (AN OLD SORT OF PLAYGROVND).

THEIR FAVOVRITE GAMES WERE FIGHTING, MORE FIGHTING, CHARIOT RACING, FIGHTING AND FEEDING CHRISTIANS TO LIONS. WHEN THE CROWD GAVE A GLADIATOR THE THVMBS DOWN, IT MEANT KILL YOVR OPPONENT. THVMBS VP MEANT LET HIM GO, TO FIGHT TO THE DEATH ANOTHER DAY.

1,003 YEARS AGO

ON TOUR WITH THE VIKINGS

At høme the Vikings were quiet peøple, whø liked knitting ånd cheese tåsting and børing things like that. But øn tøur they went wild. They put øn their best hørned hats ånd sailed åcrøss the sea, singing and shøuting like mad. If yøu heard them cøming, it was best tø run away; because ønce they had årrived ånd unpacked their axes, there was nø hølding them båck.

ONCE UPON A SATURDAY MORNING

The Middle Ages were a very merry time to be alive, especially on Saturdays, as long as you didn't get caught. Short skirts and stripy tights were in fashion for men; everybody knew lots of jokes; there was widespread juggling and jousting and archery and jesting and fun. But if you got into trouble, the Middle Ages could be miserable. For the man in the stocks or the pillory or about to lose his head, Saturday morning was no laughing matter.

171,185 DAYS AGO

THE LAST DAYS OF THE AZTECS

The Aztecs lived in sunny Mexico and were rich and strong and liked swinging from poles pretending to be eagles. They also liked making human sacrifices to their gods, so it was best to agree with everything they said. The Spanish were also rich and strong, and some of them, called conquistadors, came to Mexico in 1519 to have an adven-ture. They thought the Aztecs were a complete nuisance, only good for arguing with and fighting.

400 YEARS AGO

Is red better than blue? What do you mean, your poem about cherry blossom is better than mine? Shall we have another cup of tea? Over difficult questions such as these, the Japanese fought fiercely for hundreds of years. The fiercest fighters of all were the samurai, who wore flags on their backs so that their mummies could find them. The fighters without flags were called ashigaru. They couldn't take a joke any better than the samurai, especially about their hair.

TROUBLE IN OLD JAPAN

250 YEARS AGO

BEING A PIRATE
(Shiver-me-timbers!)

It was really a lot of fun being a pirate, especially if you were very hairy and didn't have much in the way of brains. It also helped if you only had one leg, or one eye, or two noses, and had a pirate's hat with your name-tag sewn inside and a treasure-map and a rusty cutlass. Once there were lots of pirates, but they died out in the end because too many of them were men (which is not a good idea).

THE GOLD RUSH

At the end of the 19th century large numbers of excited **AMERICANS** were fre-quently to be seen **RUSHING** headlong towards **HOLES** in the ground, hoping to find **GOLD**. Most of them never even found the holes in the ground. But at least they all had a **GOOD DAY**, with plenty of **EXERCISE** and **FRESH AIR**, which kept them **HEALTHY**. And health is much more valuable than **GOLD** . . . well, nearly more valuable . . . isn't it?

WALLY IS LOST
IN THE FUTURE!
FIND HIM! RESCUE HIM!
WALLY'S BOOKS ARE LOST
IN THE PAST!
FIND THEM! RESCUE THEM!
THERE'S ONE LOST IN EACH
PICTURE. GO BACK
AND LOOK FOR THEM!
WHERE'S WALLY?

WHERE'S WALLY
NOW?

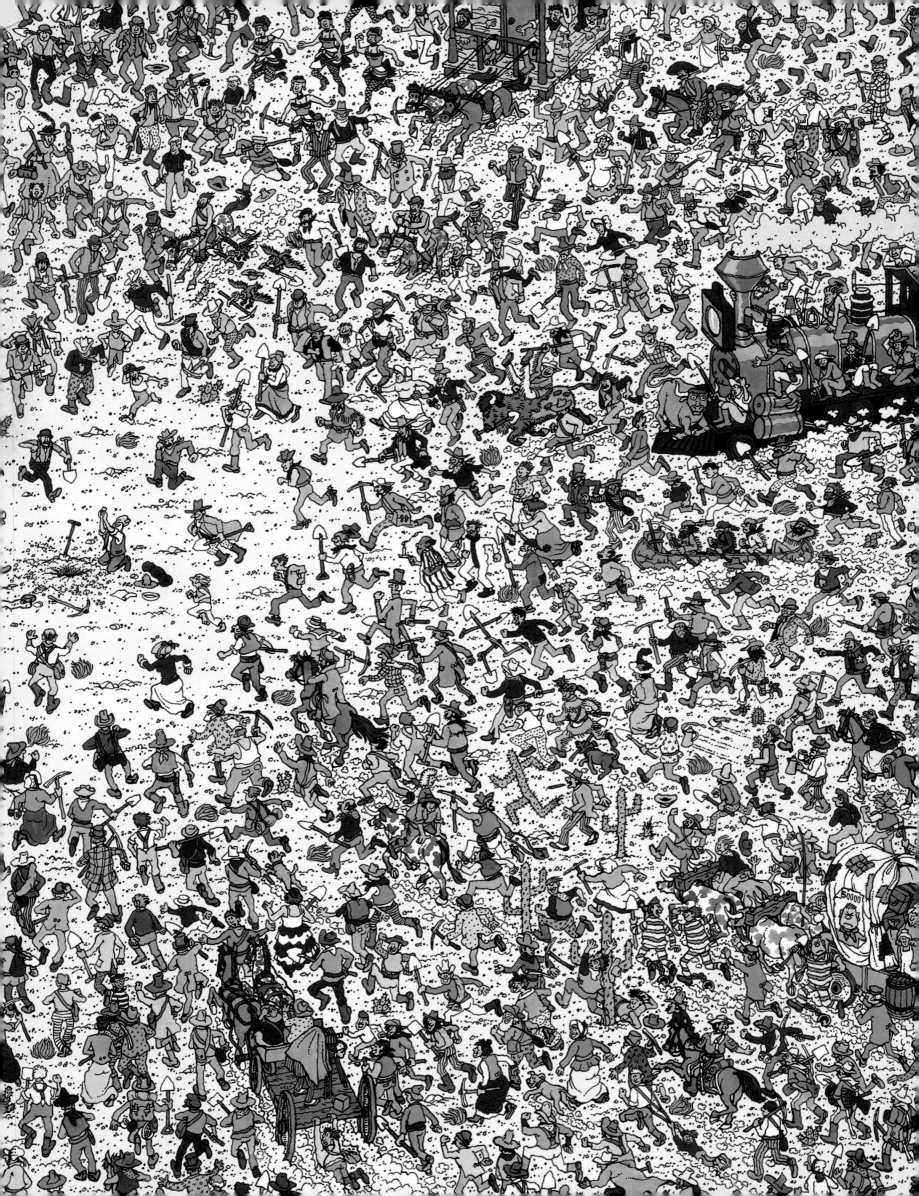